Contents

 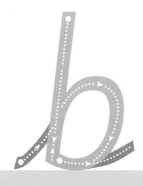 

How to use this book

Link the letter shape to the sound with the Letterland characters.

Colour letter shape.

Grey join lines.

Children can see each discrete letter shape and understand the lines required to join it to other letters.

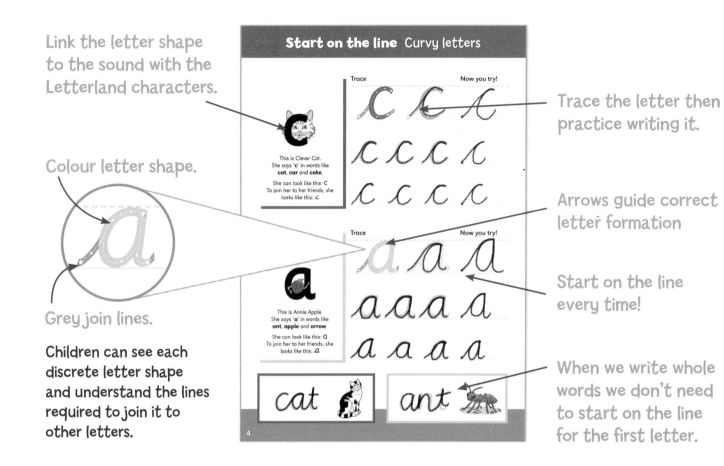

Start on the line Curvy letters

Trace   Now you try!

This is Clever Cat.
She says 'c' in words like **cat**, **car** and **cake**.

She can look like this: C
To join her to her friends, she looks like this: 𝒸

Trace   Now you try!

This is Annie Apple.
She says 'a' in words like **ant**, **apple** and **arrow**.

She can look like this: ɑ
To join her to her friends, she looks like this: 𝒶

cat   ant

4

Trace the letter then practice writing it.

Arrows guide correct letter formation

Start on the line every time!

When we write whole words we don't need to start on the line for the first letter.

Letterland Characters

There are 52 basic letter shapes in written English (**Aa–Zz**) and they are all abstract shapes. In Letterland these abstract shapes are linked to child-friendly characters that children love and quickly get to know. When your child sees these Letterland characters linked to the letter shapes, the risk of confusing all these abstract shapes is greatly reduced.

Cursive for young children

This book has been created with the font style commonly used in schools throughout the UK. Children are encouraged to 'start on the line' from as early as 4 or 5 years old. Check the style your child's school uses so you are offering the right support.

It's important for your child to learn the right 'movement pathway' for each letter. If young children are allowed to form letters 'their own way' these habits quickly become established and can be very difficult to correct later and will slow them down as they learn to write more.

Correct Handwriting Positions

Left-hander

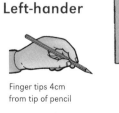

Finger tips 4cm from tip of pencil

Paper side edge
30°
Table edge

Elbows off the table
Feet on floor

Paper side edge
20°
Table edge

Chair slightly tilted
Feet on floor

Right-hander

Finger tips 2cm from tip of pencil

👉 Finger-trace

a b c d e

f g h i j

k l m n

o p q r s

t u v w

x y z

Look at how the join lines connect to each letter shape.

This is Clever Cat.
She says '**c**' in words like
cat, **car** and **cake**.

She can look like this: C
To join her to her friends, make
her look like this: *c*

Trace　　　　　　　　　　　　**Now you try!**

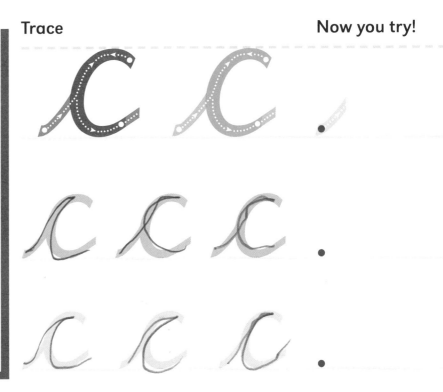

This is Annie Apple.
She says '**a**' in words like
ant, **apple** and **arrow**.

She can look like this: a
To join her to her friends, make
her look like this: *a*

Trace　　　　　　　　　　　　**Now you try!**

cat

ant

4

This is Dippy Duck.
She says '**d**' in words like
dog, **drink** and **drum**.

She can look like this: d
To join her to her friends, make
her look like this: *d*

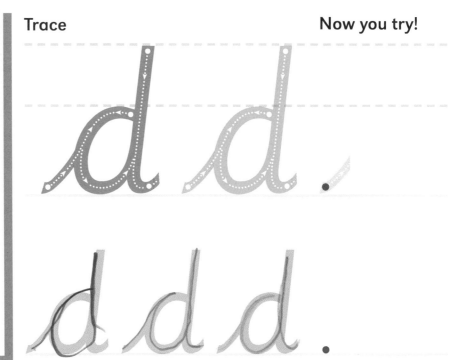

This is Oscar Orange.
He says '**o**' in words like
on, **off** and **orange**.

He can look like this: O
To join him to his friends, make
him look like this: *o*

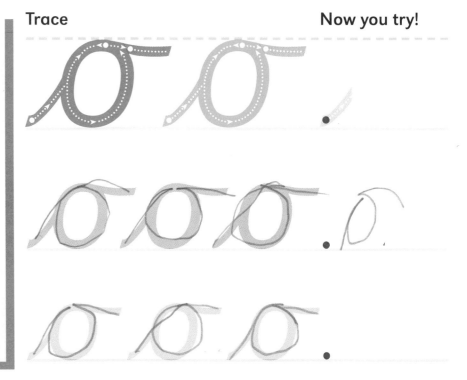

This is Golden Girl.
She says '**g**' in words like
gap, **get** and **go**.

She can look like this: g
To join her to her friends, make
her look like this: *g*

Trace

Now you try!

This is Quarrelsome Queen.
She starts words like
quick, **quit** and **quiz**.

She can look like this: q
To join her to her friends, make
her look like this: *q*

Trace

Now you try!

gap

quick

This is Sammy Snake.
He says '**s**' in words like
sad, **sand** and **sun**.

He can look like this: S
To join him to his friends, make
him look like this: _s_

sad    sun

Review – Curvy letters

c c a a d d

o o g g q q

This is Lucy Lamp Light.
She says '**l**' in words like
land, **leg** and **log**.

She can look like this: l
To join her to her friends, make
her look like this: *l*

Trace   **Now you try!**

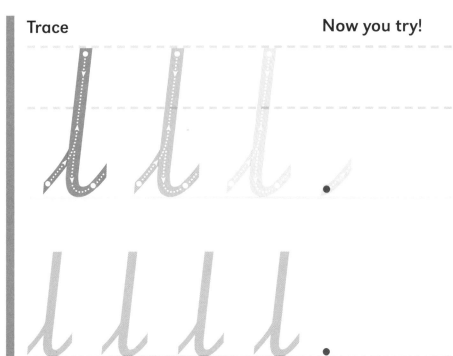

This is Talking Tess.
She says '**t**' in words like
tap, **ten** and **tin**.

She can look like this: t
To join her to her friends, make
her look like this: *t*

Trace   **Now you try!**

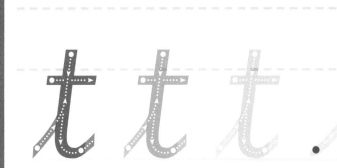

ten **10**

8

This is Harry Hat Man.
He says '**h**' in words like
hat, **hand** and **hen**.

He can look like this: h
To join him to his friends, make
him look like this: *h*

Trace

Now you try!

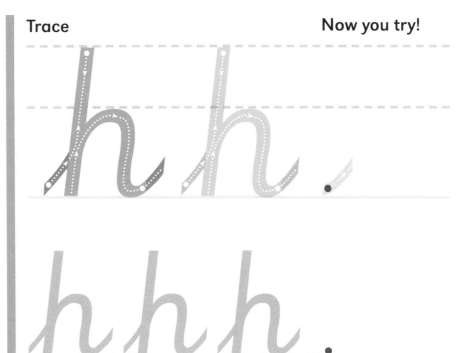

This is Bouncy Ben.
He says '**b**' in words like
bat, **bed** and **big**.

He can look like this: b
To join him to his friends, make
him look like this: *b*

Trace

Now you try!

hat

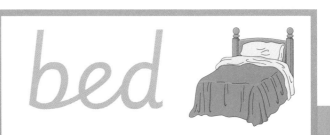

bed

Trace **Now you try!**

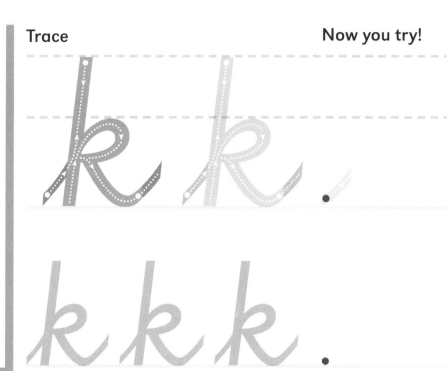

This is Kicking King.
He says '**k**' in words like
key, **kit** and **kitten**.

He can look like this: k
To join him to his friends, make
him look like this: *k*

Trace **Now you try!**

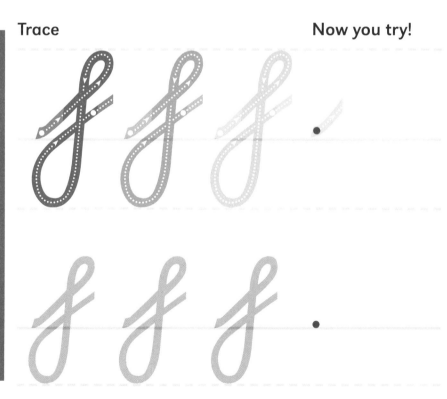

This is Firefighter Fred.
He says '**f**' in words like
fan, **flag** and **fox**.

He can look like this: f
To join him to his friends, make
him look like this: *f*

kit

fan

ι ι l l l l l l l l l l l l l

t t t t t t t t t t t t t t t

h h h h h h h h h h h

b b b b b b b b b b b b

k k k k k k k k k k k

f f f f f f f f f f f f f

Trace **Now you try!**

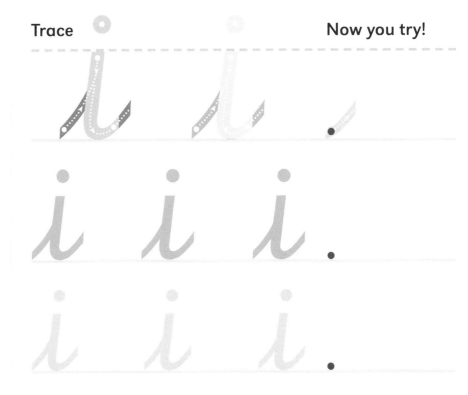

This is Impy Ink.
He says '**i**' in words like
it, **ink** and **insect**.

He can look like this: i
To join him to his friends, make
him look like this: *i*

Trace **Now you try!**

This is Uppy Umbrella.
She says '**u**' in words like
up, **unwell** and **upset**.

She can look like this: U
To join her to her friends, make
her look like this: *u*

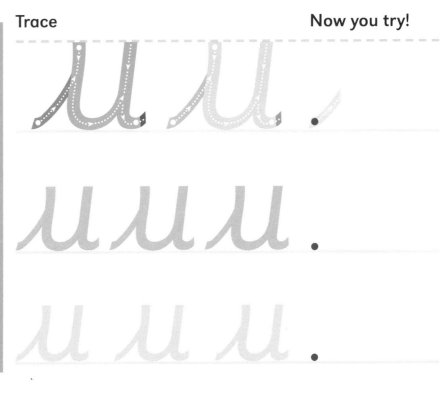

ink

up

This is Red Robot.
He says '**r**' in words like
red, **rock** and **run**.

He can look like this: r
To join him to his friends, make
him look like this: *r*

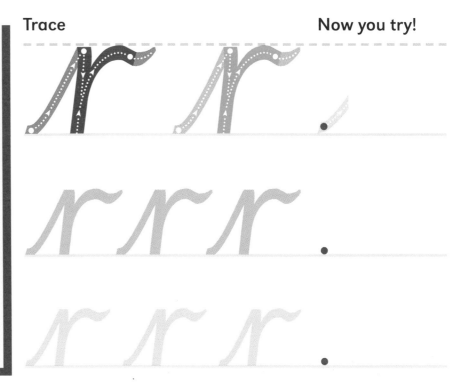

This is Noisy Nick.
He says '**n**' in words like
neck, **nest** and **net**.

He can look like this: n
To join him to his friends, make
him look like this: *n*

Trace   Now you try!

Trace

Now you try!

m m

m m m .

m m m .

This is Munching Mike.
He says '**m**' in words like
map, **milk** and **mud**.

He can look like this: m
To join him to his friends, make
him look like this: *m*

map   mud

Review - To the middle letters

i i u u r r

n n m m

This is Jumping Jim.
He says '**j**' in words like
jam, **jet** and **jug**.

He can look like this: j
To join him to his friends, make
him look like this: *j*

Trace

Now you try!

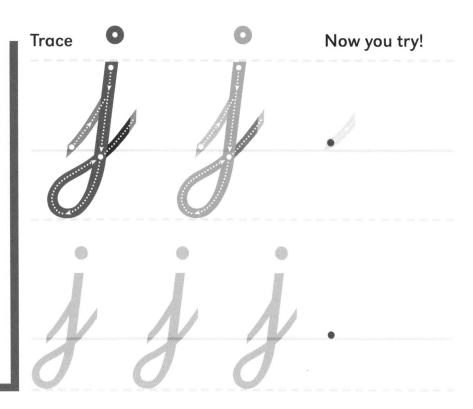

This is Peter Puppy.
He says '**p**' in words like
pen, **pet** and **pot**.

He can look like this: p
To join him to his friends, make
him look like this: *p*

Trace

Now you try!

jam

pen

Trace

Now you try!

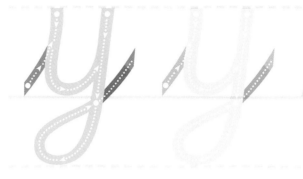

This is Yellow Yo-yo Man.
He says '**y**' in words like
yak, **yell** and **yes**.

He can look like this: y
To join him to his friends, make
him look like this: *y*

yak

yell

Review – Below the line letters

j j j j p p p

y y y

16

This is Vicky Violet.
She says 'v' in words like
van, **vet** and **visit**.

She can look like this: V
To join her to her friends, make
her look like this: 𝒩

Trace   **Now you try!**

This is Walter Walrus.
He says 'w' in words like
web, **win** and **wind**.

He can look like this: W
To join him to his friends, make
him look like this: 𝒲

Trace   **Now you try!**

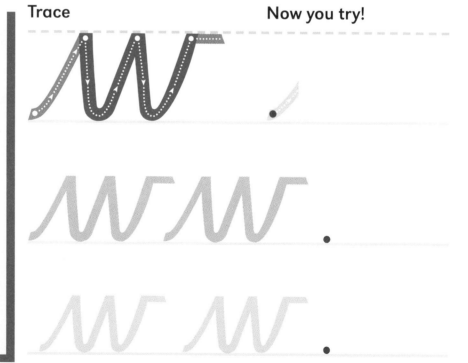

van

web

This is Fix-it Max.
He ends words like
box, **fix** and **six**.

He can look like this: X
To join him to his friends, make
him look like this: ⟋X

Trace　　　　　　　　　　　　　**Now you try!**

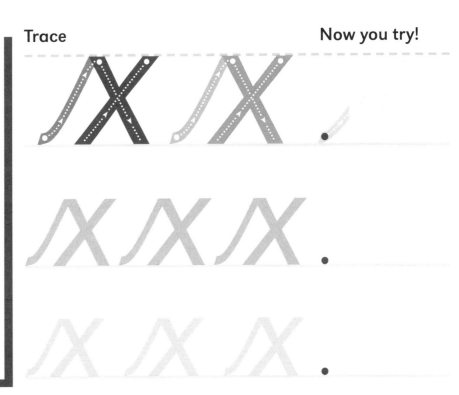

box　　　　　　　　ox

Review - Sloping line letters

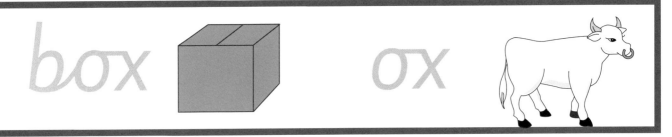

18

Trace   Now you try!

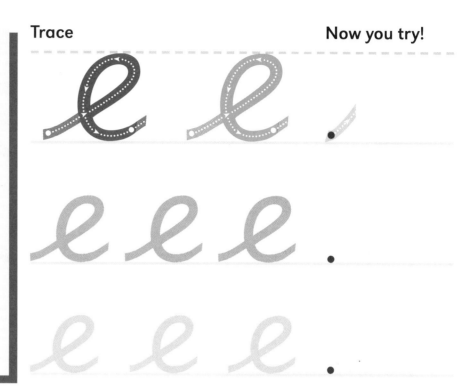

This is Eddy Elephant.
He says '**e**' in words like
egg, **elbow** and **end**.

He can look like this: e
To join him to his friends, make
him look like this: *e*

Trace   Now you try!

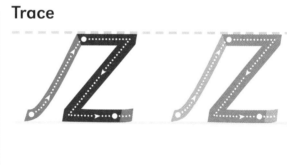

This is Zig Zag Zebra.
She says '**z**' in words like
zebra, **zero** and **zip**.

She can look like this: Z
To join her to her friends, make
her look like this: /Z

Curve starters

c a d o

Up to the top

l t h b k f

Below the line

j p y f

g s s q

To the middle

i u r n m

Slopey start

v w x

Funny starters

e z

Trace   Now you try!

 hand

 dig

 king

 bag

 cup

 hug

 bug

 sing

Trace

Now you try!

3 three

hill

clock

ill

ball

chip

chick

think

Trace   Now you try!

coat

zoo

boot

wall

van

Trace   Now you try!

doll

pot

curl

High frequency words

the	you
and	they
a	on
to	she
said	is
in	for
he	at
I	his
of	but
it	that
was	with

all	this
we	have
can	went
are	be
up	like
had	some
my	so
her	not
what	then
there	were
out	go

little

as

no

mum

one

them

do

me

down

dad

big

when

it's

see

looked

very

look

don't

come

will

into

back

from

children

him

Mr

get

just

now

came

oh

about

got

their

people

your

put

could

house

old

too

by